Explorin‑ ...
Inspiring f ...

by Pat Brunton

edited by Sally Featherstone

photographs by alc ...

The Family Learning activities in this pack formed the basis of a very successful session at the Annual Festival of the British Association for the Advancement of Science ('the BA'), held in Exeter during September 2004. The session was attended on behalf of the BA, by its President, Professor Robert Winston. The BA is delighted to be associated with pioneering work of this quality.

Exploring Together

ISBN 1 905019 31 9

978 1 905019 31 1

©Featherstone Education Ltd, 2006
Text ©Pat Brunton & Linda Thornton, 2006
Photographs ©alc associates ltd
Editor, Sally Featherstone

Little Books at Home is a trade mark of Featherstone Education Ltd.

First published in the UK, June 2006

Exploring Together has been developed from an innovative family workshop programme funded through the Copus Grant Scheme for science communication projects. The original programme ran in Treverbyn School and Treverbyn Trailblazers, St Austell, St Breock Primary School, Wadebridge and Sure Start Lescudjack in Penzance, all in Cornwall. We are grateful to parents, children and professionals in these settings for permission to reproduce the photographs in this pack.

Published in the United Kingdom by
Featherstone Education Ltd.
44 - 46 High Street
Husbands Bosworth
Leicestershire LE17 6LP

Contents

Introduction

Exploring Together is a set of four family workshop sessions on the theme of exploration and investigation. It will support professionals in the fields of early years education and childcare, parent support and family learning in delivering the five outcomes of Every Child Matters:

* be healthy
* stay safe
* enjoy and achieve
* make a positive contribution
* achieve economic wellbeing

Exploring Together is designed for families with children under the age of five and provides a wealth of opportunities to involve parents and other family members in young children's learning using ideas and resources which are interesting, intriguing and enjoyable. The workshop structure is based on ideas and activities for between 15 and 20 families, with each workshop session lasting for an hour to an hour and a half. The activities are suitable for young children, are designed to encourage parents to explore and investigate alongside their children, make use of inexpensive resources and provide lots of opportunities for conversation and discussion - for both adults and children. There are examples, comments and photographs from Exploring Together sessions run with families of children aged 0 to 5 in a variety of different settings in the South West of England.

How to use the Exploring Together resource pack

The pack has been divided into four sections to guide you through planning, organising and managing a series of family workshop sessions.

Section 1: Background Information

This section provides the background information to Exploring Together and the ideas which you will want to share with parents and families. Included in this section are: the importance of listening to children's ideas, how to encourage children to be curious, explore and investigate and ways of asking good questions and having good conversations. The information in this section could form the basis of a professional development session with staff before you run the workshops.

Section 2: Planning Exploring Together Workshops

This section explains the structure of the workshop sessions and provides a checklist to help you plan your family workshops. It highlights the key information you will want to share with parents during the workshops. Also included are comments from professionals in the fields of early years education, childcare, parent support and family learning which describe how they have adapted the basic workshop structure to suit their particular circumstances.

Section 3: Exploring Together Workshop Activities

Each Exploring Together workshop session is described in detail. The four workshops, each made up of 6 different activities are:
In the Bathroom
In the Kitchen
In the Garden
In the Community
The ideas and activities are described, the resources you need are listed and there is a handy checklist to help you keep track of your resources and consumables. Each workshop activity has its own 'prompt' card - a list of starting points and questions to help people get started. Each activity is linked to ideas to use at home found in the Little Books at Home Activity Cards.

Section 4: Useful Information

A list of useful resources and further information is included in this section. Finally, the key findings of the Sci Tot Exploring Together project 2002-2004 provide evidence which you can use to communicate the benefits of Exploring Together family workshops.

CD-Rom

This additional resource contains all the material found in Section 3 in a format that you can print out and use to support your Exploring Together family workshops.

*'I attended the SciTot Workshop **In the Bathroom** and found it to be presented in an interesting, informal and fun manner. This helped us and our children realise that science need not be all test tubes and laboratories, but that it is around us in our everyday lives. We can introduce children to science in a fun and inexpensive manner, (which is a bonus in this age of things that are sometimes too complicated and too expensive), thus stimulating their imagination and developing, hopefully, a life long interest in learning.'*

Parent, Pre School, Cornwall

Section 1: Background Information

This section explains the rationale behind the Exploring Together family workshop programme. It discusses the value of engaging with parents and carers to enhance their understanding of the importance of their role in supporting their children's learning. It highlights the importance of listening to children's ideas, encouraging them to be curious, to explore and to investigate as well as outlining ways of asking good questions and having good conversations.

You will find that the activities in the Exploring Together family workshops provide many opportunities to talk to parents and carers about being healthy, staying safe, enjoying and achieving, making a positive contribution in their community and achieving economic wellbeing for themselves and their families.

Engaging with parents and carers

Early years settings and schools are ideally placed to build the confidence of parents and family members through the relationships of trust and mutual respect which develop around the care and education of young children. For many parents the setting or school will represent their first opportunity for some considerable time to re-engage with a 'learning environment'. This phase of life can act as something of a watershed - a time to consider re-entering the world of work or a stimulus for parents to address their own learning needs to support their child's ongoing development.

The science and technology projects, activities, visits and outings which young children in your setting are involved in can also act as powerful learning situations for parents and family members and often extend their range of experiences as well those of the children. Family workshops, with adults and children playing and learning together are an ideal, non threatening way to open up the possibilities of parents extending their learning and accessing a new skills. Some parents may use this as a gateway to accredited family learning programmes and then on to focused skills development programmes. Workshops which focus on science and technology often appeal to male family members who feel comfortable sharing their expertise with their young children.

Encouraging parents to become involved in their children's learning is an essential part of making sure that young children have the best possible opportunity to enjoy and achieve. Research evidence shows that children do best in all aspects of their lives when parents and family members are actively involved in supporting them. Running family workshops as part your regular programme gives a powerful message to parents about the importance of their involvement in their child's learning.

'Exploring Together' provides opportunities for parents to be involved in your setting in a meaningful way and demonstrates the value you place on the contribution they make to their child's wellbeing, learning and development. These family workshops provide an ideal way to share the philosophy of your setting and to:

- support parents in developing an understanding of the nature of the 'curious child' to ensure that children receive consistent messages about asking questions and having good ideas;
- encourage parents to make time for opportunities and experiences that will develop their child's scientific and technological interest at home;
- explain that everyday things, found around the house, in the garden and in the local area, can be an endless source of curiosity to young children;
- talk about the importance of allowing children to take risks and make mistakes.

Children as researchers - encouraging curiosity and creativity

Children have their own ideas about how things work and why things happen - they are 'bubbling with ideas'. These ideas or theories are based on all their many different early experiences as babies and young children. Valuing these ideas, encouraging children to share them, and to listen to the ideas put forward by other children, provides the starting point for further investigations, exploration and discovery.

'I found the experience a very positive one. The children seemed to be having loads of fun but were also expressing quite complex ideas and theories surrounding the experiments'.

Parent, Day Nursery, Dorset

'This is L's big bubble. It looks like the Eden Project.'
L (age 4) made a picture of his bubble by putting a piece of paper on it. The bubble popped. Then L sucked instead of blowing.'

Curiosity is defined as 'an eager desire to know' and is a disposition for learning which should be encouraged in young children. Children can display their curiosity in many different ways, not just through the questions they ask. Curiosity will be conveyed through body language, stance and posture, or through the length of time which a child spends investigating and exploring a particular object or activity, as well as by talking. In younger children curiosity tends to be impulsive as they are attracted to new and unusual objects and situations. As they grow older their curiosity becomes more focused and you will find they pay greater attention to detail and start seeking explanations for the things they see and experience.

When children become involved in investigating and exploring they often become absorbed and will concentrate for long periods of time. You may find that they will want to re-visit a particular activity many times while they extend and consolidate their learning. In the setting you can support children's curiosity by being flexible in your approach to the allocation of time, during the course of a day or a week, or perhaps over a longer period to allow children to become involved in the long term exploration of something which particularly interests them, for example growing seeds or bird watching. Children's curiosity can be stimulated by very ordinary and inexpensive things which can be found all around, for example by discovering which things in the bathroom float and sink, or by looking at reflections in a curved spoon.

Creativity is a word most often associated with the visual and expressive arts such as painting, sculpture, music and dance. If we think of some of the most creative thinkers in the past and present, for example, Leonardo da Vinci, Albert Einstein, Stella McCartney and Bill Gates - it is clear that creativity also abounds in the fields of science and design technology.

Providing opportunities for children to express their creativity through science and technology means giving them the opportunities to talk about their ideas, make independent choices and experience the joy of discovering something new for themselves.

Listening to children and valuing their ideas

Children often have very definite ideas and theories about how the world around them works and it is worth investing time to explore their theories and thinking. These make the ideal starting points for exploration and investigation as they relate directly to the children's interests and first hand experience of the world.

Plan opportunities, and take time, to have in-depth conversations about the children's ideas and what they believe to be true. Trust them to come up with interesting possibilities for investigation and take them seriously.

Children's theories will be very creative and may not always be those which are 'accepted' by adult; they are, however, valuable because they make sense to them at the time.

Many adults find science and technology a challenge and lack confidence in their ability to support young children in this area. To help parents to feel more confident you can:

- reinforce the importance of family members as role models, expressing their interest and curiosity in the world around them;
- reassure parents that they do not need to know all the answers to children's questions - far better to find out together;

'Blackbirds take nuts to eat. They can't crack them so they drop them on the ground and let the cars run over them. When the traffic lights turn green and the car has gone they come down and pick them up.'

H age 4.

- stress the importance of parents listening to their children and respecting their ideas and theories;
- explain the importance of giving their children time - time to talk and listen, to play, to investigate and learn together and, above all, to have fun.

Being a good role model

Acting as a role model for curiosity is the best way to encourage children to be curious themselves. By being curious yourself, by thinking out loud, by saying

'I wonder why.....?'

'What would happen if ....? '

you are conveying important messages which the children will pick up.

By not 'knowing all the answers', but instead by being an enthusiastic explorer *alongside* the children, you can play a vital role in building their confidence as independent learners.

There will, inevitably, be occasions when the children need to 'borrow' the skills, knowledge and expertise of an adult. This reminds us of the importance of recognising when and how to share our skills, knowledge and understanding with children in a way which does not inhibit their personal discoveries.

> *'It was good to have qualified teaching staff and assistants as role models. Not only did they reinforce my understanding of activities, and provide support where necessary, listening to them made me more aware of how important it is to use the right language when asking questions, and give children plenty of time to think about what they are experiencing.'*
>
> *Parent, Primary School, Somerset.*

Asking good questions

Asking questions is one of the fundamental ways in which we begin discussions with children and establish the starting point of what they already know.

Making sure these are good questions requires thought, organisation, planning and lots of practice. Open questions invite children to express their thoughts and ideas, build on their previous experiences and suggest further investigation and exploration.

Remember to give children time to think and to respond - don't fill the silences with your own questions and comments - and to listen to children's responses before framing the next question.

> *'Thank you for enabling me to join in the investigation week with 'C'. I found it interesting and beneficial for both of us! The main thing I learned was to ask better questions.'*
>
> *Parent, Day Nursery, Dorset*

Open questions

Ask questions which invite children to express their thoughts and ideas.

In the Bathroom
Which brush do you think would be best for sweeping the floor?
How do you think bubbles are made?
Who do you think might use a brush like this?

In the Kitchen
What do you think will happen if we add more water to the dough?
How do you think the hand whisk works?

In the Garden
What do you think would happen if we added more water to the modelling clay?
How long do you think it will it take for the cress seeds to grow?

In the Community
What do you think would work best for building a den in the corner?
How high could you build the tower of bottles?

Remember you are not looking for the 'right' answer, instead you are establishing what the children already know, what ideas and theories they have.

You are setting the scene for investigating their ideas to enable them to find out more. By emphasising the 'you' in these questions you are giving a clear message that everyone's ideas and opinions are important.

Use questions which encourage children to talk about their past experiences.

In the Bathroom

Can you remember when we made bubble paintings?

Do you remember when we smelt all the different scented candles?

In the Kitchen

Can you remember when we made sandwiches for our picnic?

Do you remember when we lit the candles on the birthday cake?

In the Garden

What can you tell me about the seeds we planted last week?

What did the smell of lavender remind you of?

In the Community

Can you remember what we used to make our den in the garden?

What happened when we rolled the ball down the ramp?

Think of questions which pose problems and invite further investigation and exploration.

In the Bathroom

What do you think will happen when we drop the food colouring into the water?

Can you find a way to make the plasticene float?

In the Kitchen

How can we separate the stones from the sand?

Can you find a way to make the 'gloop' stick together?

In the Garden

How can we find all the bugs in the hay tray?

What happens if we plant the broad bean seed upside down?

In the Community

What sort of house can we build out of leaves and twigs?

How high can we build up a tower of bottles?

Closed questions

Using closed questions has a place - not every question needs to be open ended. In any discussion with a group of children you might also want to include attention focusing questions or measuring and counting questions.

These are some examples of closed questions which have a correct answer and can be used to build children's confidence as they can check the answers for themselves.

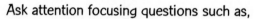

Ask attention focusing questions such as,

In the Bathroom

Have you seen the patterns the food colouring makes when you drip it onto paper?

Do you notice the different patterns the brushes make in the sand?

Can you find another brush like this one?

In the Kitchen

Have you seen the patterns inside the kiwi fruit?

Do you notice how hard the shells of the nuts are?

Can you find another fruit like this one?

In the Garden

What colour are the flowers on the primrose plants?

Can you find another leaf that is the same shape as this one?

In the Community:

Have you noticed how light the fabric is?

Have you seen what happens when you look through the red cellophane paper?

Use these measuring and counting questions

In the Bathroom

How many different brushes have we collected?

Which bubble is the biggest?

In the Kitchen

How many different vegetables have we collected?

Which piece of fruit is the biggest?

How many nuts have you threaded on the string?

What shape is the worm in the hay tray?

How big is the den we have made?

How many pieces of ribbon have we woven through the mesh?

Children's questions

Not only is it important that you, as adults, ask good questions, you also need to encourage children to ask questions themselves.

You can do this best by providing lots of opportunities for children to ask questions and valuing both their questions and their answers.

Child (age 4) -thinking out loud while adding blue food colouring to a large jar of water.

'It's gone blue. What's going to happen?

It's like fireworks.

It's making something - a dinosaur I suppose.

Adds more colouring.

'Look - it's going down to the bottom.

I wonder what?

Look, it's making seals.

I wonder what green is going to make.

Adds more colouring.

'It's made it all blue.

Look down from the top. It looks different from the top.'

Recording investigation and exploration

Encouraging the children and adults to make drawings of their investigations or to record the conversations they are having makes an important contribution to the success of the workshop sessions. Provide good quality paper and drawing pencils for both adults and children to use. Inviting adults to write down the conversations they have with their children helps them to focus on what their children are saying and how their ideas develop.

Drawing conveys meaning and can be used as a tool to initiate and communicate ideas. Some individuals who find using words difficult can express their ideas and reveal their thinking through drawing. All children will benefit from the challenge of conveying their thinking through graphic representation - pictures, plans, maps and diagrams. When a child represents her mental images in a drawing she is also re-presenting them to herself, modifying her ideas and developing reasoning skills. Explaining her drawings to an adult provides a further opportunity to revisit, revise and enrich her understanding.

Child: 'What's that?'
Adult: 'Physallis.'
Child: 'It looks like an orange. What can you see? It's big now.
Adult: 'It's clearer now. Can you say physallis?
Child: 'No I really can't'

Tom's Ginger

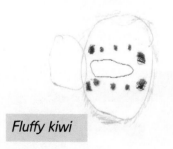

Fluffy kiwi

Taking photographs can capture the encounters, events, interactions and stages in an investigation or exploration. Revisiting these at a later date provides adults and children with the opportunity to look back on their earlier experiences and see how the children have made progress over time. Don't forget to share the visual images from your workshop with the wider community.

Section 2: Planning Exploring Together Family Workshops

Making the most of Exploring Together

Exploring Together family workshops provide opportunities for:

- building parents' confidence through activities that are linked to everyday situations, simple ideas and inexpensive resources
- parents to develop positive attitudes towards learning - both for their children and for themselves
- families to make contacts, relationships and friendships.

Exploring Together workshops can be used to support the work of early years and childcare, parent support and family learning professionals in many different settings, for example, Sure Start programmes, children's centres, day nurseries, schools and parent and toddler groups. They can be delivered in a number of different ways depending on:

- the age of the children
- the size of the group
- the availability of parents to attend workshop sessions
- the timing and structure of existing family workshop programmes.

Having used Exploring Together family workshops many professionals have commented on their value as a starting point for encouraging parents to become more involved in their children's learning.

'We focussed on two workshops - In the Kitchen and In the Bathroom. Due to the high level of parental interest both workshops were repeated. During the sessions, staff documented by use of photographs and some parents made notes of their children exploring the activities. We offered the parents a follow up session to share photographs and reflect on their children's learning.'

Teacher, Sure Start Children's Centre, Devon

'The activities have been incorporated into our 'tea time tots' sessions for under 4s, older siblings and their parents. The children enjoyed the various activities and have extended them through their own suggestions and curiosity. Language has been developed and it has been great to see parents enjoying their children through their shared exploration of new activities.'

Deputy Manager, Sure Start Local Programme, Bristol

'We ran the workshops in our Foundation and mixed Foundation/Year 1 class. Each class did a different workshop on the same day. Our intention is to rotate the activities in the summer term and to invite new children and parents who will be starting school in September. This will form part of out Welcome to Foundation package.
The biggest impact was that it involved the parents in their children's learning. I observed one father trying to work out how to separate the sand from a tub full of other mixtures. Eventually his daughter showed him what to do.'

Teacher, Primary School, Plymouth

'All the activities were ideally suited for this session - each activity was hands on and both adults and children had fun.'

Early Years Coordinator, Primary School, Somerset

'We took Exploring Together to our Under 1s groups - the parents welcomed the new experiences and the older children really got involved. The parents commented that they would never have thought of trying these ideas with their children and would certainly try them at home; they couldn't believe that their baby could be a scientist from such a young age.'

Coordinator, Sure Start Local Programme, Cornwall

'Everyone, parents, staff and children have thoroughly enjoyed the workshops and we even had our Key Stage 2/3 Science Liaison Teacher attend; she seemed to have a fantastic time investigating with the young children.'

Science Coordinator, Primary School, Devon.

'The Exploring Together workshops have been very motivating for all concerned - the Toddler Support Workers are building this type of session into their routine visits to toddler groups as they have found the interactive and participative style highly enjoyable for parents and children alike.'

Training and Development Manager Playgroup and Toddler Association, Gloucestershire

'We are making links with the Family and Parent Learning Service who are very enthusiastic about using Exploring Together Family Workshops to support their programme of adult life skills.'

Early Years Adviser, Plymouth

A guide to planning your family workshops

Use this step by step guide to help you plan the detail of your family workshop sessions:

1. Decide how you intend to incorporate Exploring Together family workshops into the work of your organisation.

   'Today showed how even the most important, yet sometimes uninteresting, subject can be made fun.'

   Parent, Sure Start Local Programme

2. Agree who will be responsible for organising and running the workshop sessions.

   'I thought science was complicated, but now I see its good fun and interesting.'   Early years professional, Cornwall

3. Identify your target audience, for example parents, male family members, home based carers, single parents and decide how best to contact them. This could be:
   - by invitation (invitations from the children themselves work well);
   - by advert or poster;
   - by word of mouth;
   - through your regular newsletter.

   a sample invitation

   Exploring Together Family Workshop
   In our Bathroom
   Please come with me to a special *Exploring Together* afternoon on:
      date:
      from: (start time to end time)
   There will be lots of interesting things for us to explore and talk about together.
      From (child's name or picture drawn by them)

   ---

4. Make sure you know how many families are coming by asking the families to book places or respond to the invitation.

5. Choose a suitable venue for the workshops. You will need a space for up to 15 families with tables and chairs which are ideally suitable for adults as well as children to use. Some of the workshop activities involve water and making 'interesting' mixtures, so make sure you are prepared for this.

6. Collect together all the resources you need for each activity well in advance. You may find it useful to use the check-lists provided with the information about each workshop in Section 3.

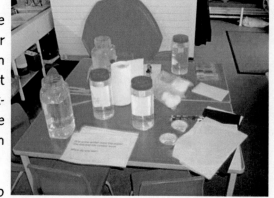

7. Allow enough time to set up the workshop activities (45 minutes to an hour) and to clear away afterwards (about half an hour). Make good use of any willing helpers.

8. Use the prompt sheets for each activity to help less confident parents begin their explorations.

9 Make sure you carry out any necessary risk assessments and health and safety checks in line with your normal policies.

10. Decide how the workshops will be staffed and explain in advance to the staff members what they are expected to do.

'Today's activities were a great chance for M and E to learn a lot and for me to learn something which I wouldn't otherwise have had the chance to do. I would thoroughly recommend it to other parents.' Parent, Pre School, Cornwall

11. Use the background information in Section 1 of this guide as the basis of a staff training session before the workshops take place.

12. Plan how you will use the Little Books at Home Activity Cards to build on the Exploring Together family workshop experience.

The structure of an Exploring Together family workshop

- A typical workshop lasts between an hour and an hour and a half.
- Set up time before the workshop - approx 45 min.
- Clearing up afterwards - approx. 30min.

Use this information to help you introduce the family workshop sessions to parents and carers.

Introducing the workshop to the families (15 - 20 min)

Ideally this introductory session should provide the opportunity to talk to family members whilst the children are being supervised by staff.

Aspects to cover in the introductory session:
- The importance of parents and carers in supporting young children's learning
- Children as researchers - encouraging curiosity and creativity
- Listening to children and valuing their ideas
- Asking good questions
- Recording investigation and exploration

In addition you will want to talk about:
- Parents taking responsibility for their own children at all times.
- Health and safety considerations - include risky freedom, small objects, hand washing, allergies.

- Encouraging the parents/carers to allow the children to take the lead as they explore and investigate together.
- Parents and children explor-
ing as many of the activities as they wish, for as long as they like.
- Using the question sheets as prompts, or starting points, if they are needed.
- Reassuring the parents they can play too, and enjoy themselves.

Exploring and investigating together (45 - 60 min)
- While the workshop is in progress staff can use the time to support parents and family groups where appropriate.
- Look for opportunities to extend the children and the adults' experiences and learning.
- Stand back and document what is happening by taking photographs, recording conversations and making notes of encounters and interactions.

Feedback and comments (10 - 15min)
Adults, children and practitioners together
- Encourage parents to share their experi-
ences. This might include comments on messy play, risky freedom, the time chil-
dren were able to concentrate and whether they would try these activities at home.
- Introduce ideas to use at home - from the Little Books at Home Activity Cards.

'We enjoyed Sci Tots, will you do it monthly, or twice monthly?
Parent, Pre School, Cornwall

What's the next session? In the kitchen? I'll have fun with that. See you...

Section 3: Exploring Together Workshop Activities

The following pages contain a range of activities for workshops with parents and their children. The CD which accompanies the pack has additional sheets for each activity for practitioners to print off, these include:

- guidelines for the organisers of the workshop
- a checklist of resources needed
- a prompt sheets for parents and carers

Each activity also identifies pages in the four Little Books at Home.
Copies can be purchased from Featherstone Education Ltd. tel: 01858 881212

In The Bathroom

This section includes the following activities:

Does it Float?
- which things float and which sink?

Bubbles, Bubbles, Bubbles
- making bubble blowers and bubble mixtures

A Basket of Brushes
- which brushes do you like?
- what are they used for?

A Basket of Smells
- which smells do you like?
- what do they remind you of?

Drops of Colour
- what happens when you drop food colouring into water?
- what happens when you drop food colouring onto paper?

Making a Boat
- building a boat which floats

Each activity has:

- guidelines for the organisers of the workshop
- a checklist of resources needed
- prompt sheets for parents and carers

'What a great morning we've just had! I really didn't know there was so much to do in the bathroom.'   **Parent, Pre School**

'Brilliant, fun and enjoyable session. Great ideas for experiments and for learning with fun and play. Would go to more sessions. Thank you Sure Start.'
Parent, Sure Start Local Programme

Does it Float?

Equipment

a large container of water - ideally a transparent plastic one, such as a plastic fish tank, so you can see through the sides. Or you could use a water tray or several large plastic bowls.

a selection of objects which float or sink, for example

corks	boat	lids
plastic boxes	sponge	foil
plasticene	plastic spoon	metal spoon
pebbles	shells	wooden bricks
potato	an apple	plastic bricks
feathers	straws	

cover for the table top

Ideas and activities to try

Put the objects one at a time into the water container.

? Which things float?

Record your answers on the floating and sinking chart.

? Can you make any of the floating things sink?   ? How?

? Can you make the sponge float?

? Can you make the sponge sink?

Try playing with the plasticene.

? Can you make the plasticene sink?

? Can you make it float?

? How?

This activity can become quite exciting - protect the table and the floor and have a mop ready to clear up any water spills!

Links to Little Books at Home Cards			Links to Little Books at Home Books	
In Our Bathroom			In Our Bathroom	
Activity Card 1	All at Sea		All at Sea	pages 6 and 7
Activity Card 4	Float or Sink		Float or Sink	pages 12 and 13
Activity Card 13	1,2,3,4,5		1,2,3,4,5	pages 30 and 31
Activity Card 16	Sail Away		Sail Away	pages 36 and 37

Does it Float?

Object	Yes	No
boat		
sponge		
plastic lid		
cork		
stone		
wooden block		
plastic spoon		
metal spoon		
shell		
apple		
potato		

Bubbles, Bubbles, Bubbles

Equipment

- shallow tray or dish for the bubble mixture
- small plastic bowls for creating 'bubble mountains'
- bubble mixture

washing up liquid	bubble wands
plastic straws	pipe cleaners
plastic coated garden wire	balloon whisk
black and red food colouring	cover for the table top

Ideas and activities to try

Investigate the bubble mixture and try blowing some bubbles.

? What do they look like?   ? What do they feel like?

? What do they sound like?   ? What do they smell like?

? How big a bubble can you blow?

? Can you use the garden wire to make a square wand?

? Does it make a square bubble?

? Can you make coloured bubbles?

? How big a bubble mountain can you make?

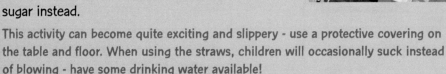

A recipe for bubble mixture:

3 parts washing up liquid

7 parts warm water

1 part glycerine or sugar

Glycerine helps the bubbles last longer by preventing them from drying out. If you can't get glycerine, use sugar instead.

This activity can become quite exciting and slippery - use a protective covering on the table and floor. When using the straws, children will occasionally suck instead of blowing - have some drinking water available!

Links to *Little Books at Home* Cards		Links to *Little Books at Home* Books	
In Our Bathroom		In Our Bathroom	
Activity Card 2	Blow it	Blow it	pages 8 and 9
In Our Kitchen		In Our Kitchen	
Activity Card 7	Fun with water	Fun with water	pages 18 and 19

A Basket of Brushes

Equipment

small basket for your brush collection
small tray of fine sand
washing up brush
paint brush
shaving brush
hair brush
bottle brush
shoe/suede brush
scrubbing brush
pastry brush
small sweeping brush
long pile fur fabric

Ideas and activities to try

Try sorting the brushes.
? Which brushes are soft?
? Which brushes are hard?

Talk about the different brushes.
? What do you think they are used for?
? Which brush do you like the best?
? Why?

Try using the different brushes in the tray of sand.
? What sort of patterns can you make?

Use some of the different brushes on the fur fabric.
? Which ones work best?

Links to *Little Books at Home* Cards		Links to *Little Books at Home* Books	
In Our Bathroom		In Our Bathroom	
Activity Card 5	Bathroom Basket	Bathroom Basket	pages 14 and 15
Activity Card 6	A Brush Collection	A Brush Collection pages 16 and 17	
In Our Garden		In Our Garden	
Activity Card 10	Lets Get Wet	Lets Get Wet!	pages 27 and 28

A Basket of Smells

Equipment

small cane basket for the objects and some of these:

small scented soaps   pot pourri mixture

bath oil - lavender, rose, lemon, orange

scented candles - lavender, rose, lemon, orange

sprigs of lavender

rose flower - choose one with a strong scent

lemon and/or orange

a selection of empty perfume bottles

bath salts

bowl of water

Ideas and activities to try

Investigate the things in the basket.

? Which smells do you like?

? Which smells don't you like?

? Can you make up words to describe the different smells?

Smell the different things in the basket.

? Can you recognise what they smell like?

? Can you match the things which smell the same?

Investigate the perfume bottles.

? Do you like the smell of the perfume bottles?

? Which ones do you like the best?

? Are there two which smell the same?

Drop some bath salts into water.

? What happens?

? What does it smell like?

? Does the smell go away?

Links to *Little Books at Home* Cards		Links to *Little Books at Home* Books	
In Our Bathroom		In Our Bathroom	
Activity Card 7	Smelly Stuff	Smelly Stuff	pages18 and 19
Activity Card 10	You Smell Great	You Smell Great	pages 24 and 25
Activity Card 11	The Body Shop	The Body Shop	pages 26 and 27

Drops of Colour

Equipment

large transparent plastic jars full of water

plastic pipettes; food colouring - several colours

foil   cotton wool balls   make up remover pads

fabric that is water resistant - plastic or rubber coated

fabric that will absorb water - cotton or woollen

kitchen paper or coffee filter paper   cover for the table top

Ideas and activities to try

Use the plastic pipette to drop some food colouring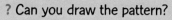
into the water in the jar. Watch carefully to see
what happens. Talk about the patterns the food
colouring makes.

> ? Can you draw the pattern?

> ? Does it look the same from above and from the side?

Now shake the jar carefully. Add another colour.

> ? What happens?

Drip some water onto the different materials - fabrics, foil, cotton wool,
paper.

> ? What do you see? Do all the drops look the same?

Drop some food colouring onto dry kitchen paper. Talk about what you see.

> ? What happens if you carefully drip water onto the drop
of colour? Drop some food colouring onto <u>wet</u> kitchen
paper. What happens?

> ? Do all the colours behave in the same way?

Use a protective covering on the table and remind parents that food colouring will stain
hands and clothing. Hands can be washed, but the colour may be permanent on some
clothing fabrics!

Links to *Little Books at Home* Cards		Links to *Little Books at Home* Books	
In Our Bathroom		In Our Bathroom	
Activity Card 3	Fill It Up	Fill It Up	pages 10 and 11
Activity Card 9	Beautiful Faces	Beautiful Faces	pages 22 and 23
Activity Card 14	Listen	Listen!	pages 32 and 33

Making a Boat

Equipment

water tray or plastic aquarium

foil	plastic boxes	plastic bottle tops
lids	plasticene	lolly sticks
straws	thick paper	soap dish
cardboard	wood offcuts	string
elastic bands	glue	
small world play figures		cover for the table top
photographs and pictures of boats		

Ideas and activities to try

Look closely at the pictures of boats

Talk about what you can see.

Try making your own boat from the materials on the table.

? What would you need to use?

Try floating your boat in the water.

? Does it float well?

? Is it stable or does it tip over?

? Will it carry the play people?

? Can you make your boat move?

? How?

This activity can become quite exciting - use a protective covering on the table!

Links to *Little Books at Home* Cards	Links to *Little Books at Home* Books
In Our Bathroom	In Our Bathroom
Activity Card 13 1,2,3,4,5	1,2,3,4,5 pages 30 and 31
Activity Card 16 Sail Away	Sail Away ! pages 36 and 37

In The Kitchen

This section includes the following activities:

Mixing, Mixing, Mixing
- investigating mixtures, what they feel like and how they behave

Separating Mixtures
- finding the best tool for the job

Exploring Kitchen Tools
- looking at simple mechanisms and finding out how tools work

Changing, Changing
- what does jelly feel like?
- what happens to chocolate when it warms up and cools down?

Fruit and Vegetables
- looking closely at the inside and outside of different types of fruit and vegetables

Making sandwiches:
- making choices, using tools and behaving safely

Each activity has:
- guidelines for the organisers of the workshop
- a checklist of resources needed
- prompt sheets for parents and carers

'These are such simple ideas which the children are enjoying so much, we should do more of this at home.'   Father, Sure Start Local Programme

'Magnifying glasses can show that things have shapes and colours that you don't notice at first.'   Parent, Primary School, Somerset

Mixing, Mixing, Mixing

Equipment

large mixing bowls   measuring spoons

measuring jug   rolling pins   flat trays

mixing spoons   dough cutters   flour

cornflour   water   salt

rice, sand or dried coconut   food colouring

Ideas and activities to try

Making dough

Put 2 measures of flour and 1 measure of salt into a mixing bowl. Add 1 measure of water and stir to mix everything together. When the mixture forms a lump take it out of the bowl. Knead it with your hands until it's smooth.

? What does the dough feel like?

? Is it sticky or dry?

? What does it smell like?

Try rolling it out using a rolling pin.

? How thin can you roll it? Can you pick it up?

Now try adding some sand or rice or coconut to your dough.

? What does it feel like now?

Making gloop

Sprinkle some cornflour into a flat tray. Add water a little at a time and mix it with your fingers.

? What does it feel like? Do you like the feeling?

? What does it look like?

? What happens when you add more water?

? What happens when you add more cornflour?

Be aware that a small number of children may be allergic to wheat in flour!

Links to *Little Books at Home* Cards		Links to Little Books at Home Books	
In Our Kitchen		In Our Kitchen	
Activity Card 3	Goopy Mixtures	Goopy Mixtures	pages 10 and 11
Activity Card 10	Add Something	Add Something!	pages 24 and 25
Activity Card 15	Dough Fun	Dough Fun	pages 36 and 37
In Our Garden		In Our Garden	
Activity Card 11	Fun in the Rain	More Fun in the Rain pages 30 and 31	

Separating Mixtures

Equipment

      flat trays, bowls or small plastic boxes for the mixtures.

      a variety of spoons, large and small, with holes and without holes

sieves	colanders	chopsticks
tweezers	dried peas and beans	rice
pasta shapes	lentils	small stones
large polished stones		sand
magnifying glasses		

Ideas and activities to try

Make a mixture with lots of different things in it. Investigate the mixture.

      ? What does it look like?

       Use a magnifying glass to look closely

      ? What can you see?

      ? What does it feel like?

      ? Can you separate out the different things in the mixture?

      ? Which tools are the best to help with this?

Don't use dried red kidney beans in this activity - the beans should not be handled by children until thoroughly cooked!

Links to *Little Books at Home* Cards	Links to *Little Books at Home* Books
In Our Kitchen	In Our Kitchen
Activity Card 12 Mix and Sort	Mix and Sort pages 30 and 31

Exploring Kitchen Tools

Equipment

hand whisk	balloon whisk
egg beater	mixing spoons
can opener	

a plastic gear set such as LEGO Fun Time Gears or Georello

Ideas and activities to try

Look at the different kitchen tools
>   ? What are they for?
>   ? How do you think they work?

Investigate the plastic gears in the set.
>   ? Can you make things turn using the gears?
>   ? Which way do the gears turn?
>   ? How many gears can you link together?
>   ? Do they all turn in the same direction?
>   ? Can you use the gears to make a model that moves?

Links to *Little Books at Home* Cards		Links to *Little Books at Home* Books	
In Our Kitchen		In Our Kitchen	
Activity Card 5	Spot the Holes	Spot the Holes	pages 14 and 15
Activity Card 16	Light or Heavy	Light or Heavy	pages 38 and 39
In Our Bathroom		In Our Bathroom	
Activity Card 8	Heavy and Light	Heavy and Light	pages 20 and 21

Changing, Changing

Equipment

measuring jug   mixing bowls, large and small

mixing spoons   teaspoons   warm water   foil

jelly   chocolate   pasta   dried noodles

or spaghetti   shaped cutters   trays of made up jelly

'Sticky wiggles' - these are made of cornstarch and sometimes used as packaging material

Ideas and activities to try

Investigate the jelly in the tray.

> ? What does it look like? What does it
> feel like? What does it smell like?
> ? Can you cut out shapes from the jelly?

Investigate the chocolate.

> ? What does it look like? What does it
> feel like? What does it smell like?

Try breaking the chocolate up into small pieces. Put some pieces of chocolate into a small bowl. Now pour some warm water into a larger bowl and stand the small bowl in it. Watch the chocolate carefully.

> ? What happens to it?

Stir the chocolate gently with a spoon and try dropping some onto a piece of foil. Watch carefully.

> ? What happens?

Investigate the 'Sticky wiggles'.

> ? What does it look like? What does it feel like? What does it smell like?

Dip one end of a wiggle in water and then stick it onto a piece of paper.

Add more to make your own creation. Try dripping some water onto your sculpture. What happens?

Links to *Little Books at Home* Cards		Links to *Little Books at Home* Books	
In Our Kitchen		In Our Kitchen	
Activity Card 5	Spot the Holes	Where's it Gone?	pages 6 and 7
Activity Card 16	Light or Heavy	Watch it Melt	pages 8 and 9
In Our Bathroom		Freezing Cold!	pages 20 and 21
Activity Card 8	Heavy and Light	Icy Fingers	pages 32 and 33

Fruit and Vegetables

Equipment

large stand magnifier hand magnifiers   small mirrors
cutting board   sharp knife
nutcrackers with different mechanisms   feely bag
a selection of fruit, for example orange, apple, banana, kiwi fruit, physallis, pomegranate
a selection of vegetables, for example carrot, potato, onion, leek, sprout, parsnip
mixed nuts in their shells

Ideas and activities to try

Investigate the fruit and the vegetables
? What does each one look like?
? What does each one feel like?
? What does each one smell like?

Cut one of the fruits or vegetables in half
? What does it look like inside?

Use the magnifier to look really closely. Try drawing a picture of what you see. Try using the nutcrackers.

Play a guessing game using the 'feely bag'.
? Can you guess what fruit or
vegetable is in the bag just by
feeling?

Talk to the parents about safety when using the sharp knife.
Explain the importance of children learning to use tools correctly!

Links to *Little Books at Home* Cards	Links to *Little Books at Home* Books
In Our Kitchen	In Our Kitchen
Activity Card 6 Fruity Fingers	Fruity Fingers pages 16 and 17
Activity Card 14 Veggie Prints	Veggie Prints pages 34 and 35

Making Sandwiches

Equipment

cutting board	sharp knife	grater
bowls	shaped cutters	paper plates
table napkins	plastic knives	sliced brown bread
sliced white bread	spread	cheese
cucumber	iceberg lettuce	bananas

Ideas and activities to try

Investigate the bread and the sandwich fillings and talk about the different choices that are available.

? What sort of bread do you like?

? What sort of filling do you like?

Choose the ingredients you like and make some sandwiches. Talk about the different stages in making a sandwich. Try cutting the sandwiches into different shapes.

Draw a picture of the sandwiches you have made.

? Which sandwich do you like the best?

This activity involves making something which the children and adults can eat. All the tools and equipment should be suitable for the job and clean. Make sure everyone washes their hands before starting to make their sandwiches!

Links to *Little Books at Home* Cards	Links to *Little Books at Home* Books
In Our Kitchen	In Our Kitchen
Activity Card 9 Cook with Water	Cook with Water pages 22 and 23
In Our Community	In Our Community
Activity Card 13 Let's Make a Picnic	Let's Make a Picnic pages 30 and 31

In The Garden

This section includes the following activities:

Planting Broad Beans and Cress
- looking at seeds over time to watch them sprout and grow

Looking at Plants
- looking closely at the shape, texture, colour and smell of different plants

Making Models
- investigating clay - what it feels like and what it will do

Feed the Birds
- making a simple bird feeder

Lifting and Shifting
- using a large scale construction kit to make a working model

The Hay Tray
- what might be hiding under the ground?

Each activity has:
- guidelines for the organisers of the workshop
- a checklist of resources needed
- prompt sheets for parents and carers

'I am so pleased to be able to spend time in the garden together and have so much fun' **Parent, Toddler Group**

'I didn't think this could be such fun, better than at school.'
Father, Baby and Toddler Group

Planting Broad Beans and Cress

Equipment

glass petri dishes   clear plastic beakers

blotting paper   cotton wool   dry broad bean seeds

some broad beans that have been soaked in water overnight

cress seeds   pictures and photographs of seeds and plants

Ideas and activities to try

Planting broad beans

1. Look together at the two containers of broad
beans seeds.
   ? What is the difference?
   Talk about why they are different.
2. Open up a broad bean and look inside.
   ? How many different parts can you see
   inside the seed? Use the magnifier to
   help you.
   ? Can you draw a picture of the inside of the seed?
3. Choose a broad bean seed to plant.
   Cut some blotting paper to fit around the inside the plastic beaker.
   Slide your broad bean seed between the blotting paper and the side of the
   plastic container.
   Pour some water into the container.
   Watch carefully to see what happens to the blotting paper. The seed is now
   ready to take home.

At home: Keep the blotting paper damp. Check your seed together every day to see
what happens to it. Try drawing pictures or taking photographs of your seed as it grows.

Planting cress

1. Look together at the cress seeds. Help your child to spread some cotton wool
over the bottom of a plastic Petri dish. Try to make it as flat as possible.
2. Pour in some water to make the cotton wool damp.
3. Sprinkle some cress seeds over the cotton wool. Try to spread them out.
4. Put the lid on the Petri dish to keep the seeds safe on the way home.

At home: Take the lid off, put the dish in a warm, light place and keep the cotton
wool damp.Check the seeds every day with your child, talk about what you can see
happening as the seeds start to grow. Draw pictures and take photos of the cress
seeds as they grow.

Links to Little Books at Home Cards		Links to Little Books at Home Books	
In Our Garden		In Our Garden	
Activity Card 2	Will it Grow?	Will it Grow?	pages 10 and 11
Activity Card 7	Seeds Everywhere	Seeds Everywhere	pages 22 and 23

Looking at Plants

Equipment

ferns - a variety of different shapes   succulents

primrose/pansy or other flowering plants

plants with variegated leaves and plants with long 'spiky' leaves

a selection of herbs - basil, rosemary, sage, curry plant, thyme, mint

lavender, scented leaf geraniums

magnifiers   colouring pencils   fine line colouring pens

photographs of plants and flowers   drawing pads or clipboards

Ideas and activities to try

Look carefully at the different types of plants and flowers, and the different parts of the plants.

? What shape are the leaves?   ? What colour are the leaves?

? Do they have patterns on them?   ? What do the leaves feel like?

? Do the leaves smell of anything?   ? Do you like the smell?

? Does it remind you of anything?   ? Does the plant have flowers?

? Do the flowers smell?

? Can you see the roots of any of the plants?

? What do they look like?

Try drawing some pictures of your favourite plant.

Look at the photographs of plants and flowers.

? Are any of then the same as the ones you have in front of you?

Links to *Little Books at Home* Cards	Links to *Little Books at Home* Books
In Our Kitchen	In Our Kitchen
Activity Card 11 Make Your Mark	Make Your Mark pages 28 and 29

Making Models

Equipment

modelling clay   small clay plant pots   flowers or plants
models of insects or animals   plastic knife
small bowl for water
photographs of plants and flowers
pictures of snails, ants, butterflies and worms

Ideas and activities to try

With your child, spend some time exploring the clay and seeing what you can do with it. Talk about:

? What does it feel like?   ? What does it look like?
? What does it smell like?

Work the clay into different shapes:

? Can you roll it into balls?   ? Can you cut it into slabs?
? Can you shape it into coils, or worms?

Investigate joining pieces of clay. Try using a little water to help to stick the pieces together.

? What does the clay feel like when you add more water to it?

Encourage your child to think about what sort of model he/she would like to make with the clay. Make a model yourself, alongside your child. Talk together about what you are doing as you make your models.

The model you make could be a plant, a flower, a small pot, a seed, a spider, a snail, a worm, a butterfly........ or an idea of your own.

Links to *Little Books at Home* Cards	Links to *Little Books at Home* Books
In Our Garden	In Our Garden
Activity Card 13 Let's go to the Beach	Let's go to the Beach pages 34 and 35
Activity Card 14 Sand Art	Sand Art pages 36 and 37

Feed the Birds

Equipment

peanuts in their shells

twine or strong wool

photographs of birds and bird feeders

bodkins or big needles

garden wire

Ideas and activities to try

Making a peanut string

1. Help your child to thread the wool or twine onto the bodkin.

2. Tie a big knot in the end.

3. Carefully push the bodkin through the middle of the peanut shells.

4. Thread the shells onto the twine until you have a long string.

5. You could try threading the nuts on to a length of garden wire instead.

6. Tie a loop in the top of the string so you can hang it up outside.

7. The peanut string is now ready to take home and hang up for the birds.

Be aware that some children and adults are allergic to nuts. Check carefully in advance and do not include this activity in your workshop if you have anyone in the setting with a nut allergy!

Links to *Little Books at Home* Cards	Links to *Little Books at Home* Books
In Our Garden	In Our Garden
Activity Card 15 Make a Pond	Make a Pond pages 38 and 39
In Our Community	In Our Community
Activity Card 6 Make Bird Feeders	Make Bird Feeders pages 16 and 17

Lifting and Shifting

Equipment

Maxamec, or other large scale construction kit
small model of a teddy pushing a wheelbarrow
straw hat   plastic flower
large teddy bear   drawing paper
drawing pencils   disposable camera

watering can
child size trowel
fine felt tip pens

Ideas and activities to try

Try using the construction kit to make a barrow to help Teddy carry his tools around the garden.

Investigate the construction kit with your child. Look at the different pieces in the kit and talk about what they do. Investigate how the pieces fit together.

Talk about the things which Teddy will need to carry in his barrow.

    ? What are they used for?

    ? What sort of barrow would you like to make?

You could make a drawing of your barrow before you start.

Now use the construction kit to make the barrow you have drawn.

Talk with your child about what you both doing as you help each other make the barrow together.

Take photographs of your barrow as you are making it.

Try your barrow out when it is finished.

    ? Does it work well?

    ? Are there any ways you could make it better?

Photograph your barrow when it is finished.

Links to *Little Books at Home* Cards		Links to *Little Books at Home* Books	
In Our Garden		In Our Garden	
Activity Card 16	Digger	Digger	pages 40 and 41
In Our Kitchen		In Our Kitchen	
Activity Card 4	Unpack Boxes	Unpack Boxes	pages 12 and 13

The Hay Tray

Equipment

builder's tray or clean cat litter tray

non allergenic hay or straw (from a pet shop)   soil or compost

potting compost	pea gravel	sand
stones	coins	broken plant pot pieces
glass nuggets	plastic worms, insects, spiders, butterflies, caterpillars	
small sieves	scoops and spoons	tongs
chopsticks	magnifiers	

photographs of insects, ants, worms and snails

Ideas and activities to try

Look at the hay tray with your child.

? What can you see in it?

? What do you think might be in the tray?

Investigate the layer of hay.

? What can you find?

Talk about all the different things you find in the hay.

? What do you think might be hiding in the soil layer under the hay?

Help your child to investigate carefully using the small spoons and sieves.

Talk about the different things you find.

? How do you think they got there?

Encourage your child to draw pictures of the different things you have found in the tray.

Draw some pictures yourself.

As you draw together talk to your child about all the different things you might find under the ground.

Use fresh compost and new hay!

Links to *Little Books at Home* Cards	Links to *Little Books at Home* Books
In Our Garden	In Our Garden
Activity Card 6 What a Surprise	What a Surprise pages 18 and 19
Activity Card 8 Excavate	Excavate! pages 24 and 25

In Our Community

This section includes the following activities:

Making a Den
- choosing the best materials to make a den

Build it Up
- building towers that stay up, and fall down

Homes
- looking closely at natural materials

Looking Through
- seeing the world in a different way

Weaving
- using reclaimed and natural materials to make patterns and pictures

Rolling, Rolling, Rolling
- which objects rolls the furthest?
- which objects roll the fastest?

Each activity has:
- guidelines for the organisers of the workshop
- a checklist of resources needed
- prompt sheets for parents and carers

'Excellent ideas to use at home - and at Gran's!'   **Parent, Pre School**

'I think at some points I was enjoying it more than 'K'. It was a good experience and I hope there are more in the future.'   **Parent, Sure Start Children's Centre**

'Great fun, will definitely come again.'   **Parent, Pre School**

Making a Den

Equipment

large pieces of fabric of different weights, textures and thicknesses

clothes airer	clothes pegs	soft elastic bands - hair ties
ropes	twine, rope, string	bamboo canes
garden ties		

Ideas and activities to try

Have a look at the different types of fabric and material.

Investigate the fabrics and talk about how they look and feel.

? Which do you think would be best for making a den?

? What else might you need?

Try building a den together.

? How do you think you could hold the pieces together?

? What do you think it will be like inside the den?

Crawl inside and find out.

? Can you build a wigwam?

Links to *Little Books at Home* Cards	Links to *Little Books at Home* Books
In Our Garden	In Our Garden
Activity Card 2 Will it Grow?	Our Place pages 8 and 9
Activity Card 7 Seeds Everywhere	Shady Places pages 32 and 33

Build it up

Equipment

empty plastic water bottles

plastic Ribena or other juice bottles (the stumpy, wide necked sort)

objects to put into the bottles:

> sequins, feathers, straws, beads, buttons,
> pebbles, sand, glass nuggets, coloured water

pictures and photographs of tall buildings

Ideas and activities to try

Investigate the different bottles and talk about what is inside them.

? Which ones are light?

? Which ones are heavy?

? Which ones make a noise?

? Which ones have liquid in?

? Which one do you like best?

Add some objects to the bottles.

? What happens to the sound?

? Can you build a tower with the bottles?

? How high can you build it?

? Which bottles should go at the bottom?

Links to *Little Books at Home* Cards		Links to *Little Books at Home* Books	
In Our Garden		In Our Garden	
Activity Card 5	Builders at Work	Builders at Work	pages 16 and 17
In Our Kitchen		In Our Kitchen	
Activity Card 4	Unpack Boxes	Unpack Boxes	pages 12 and 13

Homes

Equipment

builders tray	pebbles	shells
leaves	twigs	straw
wood shavings	raffia	seed pods
cones	Oasis	garden netting
garden ties		

Ideas and activities to try

Investigate the different objects in the tray and talk about them.

? What do you think they are?

? Where might they come from?

? What do they feel like?

? What do they smell like?

? Could you use some of the objects to build a house?

? What do you think you might use?

? Who might live in the house you have built?

Links to *Little Books at Home* Cards	Links to *Little Books at Home* Books
In Our Community	In Our Community
Activity Card 5 In Our Street	In Our Street pages 14 and 15
In Our Garden	In Our Garden
Activity Card 13 Let's Go To The Beach	Let's Go To The Beach pages 34 and 35

Looking Through

Equipment

coloured plastic
plastic bottles with coloured water
cellophane
bubble wrap
transparent plastic
sunglasses

Ideas and activities to try

Have a look at the different types of fabric and material.

Investigate the fabrics and talk about how they look and feel.

Investigate the different materials by looking through them.

? Can you see through all of them?

? What does it look like when you look through them?

? Which one can you see through best?

? What happens when you look through the coloured plastic?

? What happens when you look through the sunglasses?

Warn children and adults never to look directly at the sun!

Links to *Little Books at Home* Cards		Links to *Little Books at Home* Books	
In Our Community		In Our Community	
Activity Card 1	Bonfire Night in the Park	Bonfire Night in the Park	pages 6 and 7
Activity Card 2	Sunny Day	On a Sunny Day	pages 8 and 9
Activity Card 8	Here's the Weather Forecast	Here's the Weather Forecast	pages 20 and 21
In Our Bathroom		In Our Bathroom	
Activity Card 12	Look At Me	Look At Me	pages 28 and 29

Weaving

Equipment

garden mesh	garden netting	ribbons
shredded paper strips		wool
string	raffia	twigs and bark

natural materials - sheeps' wool, feathers, grasses, leaves, flowers

Ideas and activities to try

? Could you use the different resources to weave a pattern?

? What could you use to make the pattern?

? What would be best to thread the pieces through?

? What patterns can you make?

? Which materials would you like to use for your pattern?

? Can you draw the pattern you have made?

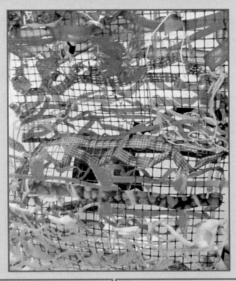

Links to *Little Books at Home* Cards	Links to *Little Books at Home* Books
In Our Community	In Our Community
Activity Card 7 Let's do it Outside!	Let's do it Outside! pages 18 and 19
Activity Card 10 Carnival!	Carnival! pages 24 and 25
In Our Garden	In Our Garden
Activity Card 4 Music Time	Music Time pages 14 and 15

Rolling, Rolling, Rolling

Equipment

wooden plank to use as a slope
balls of different weights and sizes
fruit and vegetables of different shapes:
> orange, lemon, banana, potato, carrot, turnip, apple

toy cars
round objects

Ideas and activities to try

Set up the plank to make a slope to roll things down.

? Which things do you think will roll down the slope easily?

? Which things won't roll down?

Try out your ideas and see what happens

? What happens if you lift the slope up
> higher?

? Which things do you think roll the best?

? Can you tell which things roll the fastest?

? Which things roll straight and which
> things roll in a wiggly line?

Section 4: Useful Information

alc associates ltd

Pat Brunton and Linda Thornton provide professional development and consultancy through alc associates ltd for Local Authorities, Sure Start Programmes, early years and childcare settings, nurseries and schools. They focus on exploration and investigation and family involvement in their children's learning. Training on delivering **Exploring Together Family Workshops** is available. Please phone 01872 264603, contact info@alcassociates.co.uk or visit the website www.alcassociates.co.uk for details.

Little Books at Home

The *Little Books at Home* series consists of four books and four packs of Activity Cards:

> In Our Bathroom
> In Our Kitchen
> In Our Garden
> In Our Community

Little Books at Home are based on ideas from the very successful Little Books series, specially adapted for parents and carers. The activities within them are easy to set up, don't need any special equipment and have been chosen to promote home learning for young children. Each set of *Little Books at Home* Activity Cards contains a selection of 16 favourite Little Books at Home activities. With one activity to a laminated card, they make ideal resources for parents, childminders, carers, family support workers and toy libraries. The guidance leaflet for the set gives ideas and tips for use, and includes a photocopiable record sheet to keep track of who has used each card.

Little Books at Home and the *Little Books at Home* Activity Cards can be used to support parents exploring and investigating with their children at home. You could:

- use them to support the family workshop activities;
- set up a lending library of ideas and resources;
- incorporate them into family learning programmes.

Little Books at Home and *Little Books at Home* Activity Cards are available from

Featherstone Education, 01858881212

www.featherstone.uk.com

Little Books

The authors of Exploring Together, Linda Thornton and Pat Brunton, have written a number of *Little Books* for Featherstone Education. In common with all the titles in the *Little Books* series, they have been designed to support an investigative approach to young children's learning.

They are:

- Little Book of Light and Shadow   LB 25
- Little Book of Time and Place   LB 31
- Little Book of Living Things   LB 37
- Little Book of Seasons   LB 44
- Little Book of Treasureboxes   LB 47

There are fifty titles in the *Little Books* series. Contact Featherstone Education for a full list. The titles above are also available from alc associates ltd.

The British Association for the Advancement of Science (the BA)
www.the-ba.net

The BA (British Association for the Advancement of Science) exists to advance the understanding, accessibility and accountability of the sciences and engineering. It seeks to achieve this by connecting science with people: promoting openness about science in society and affirming science as a prime cultural force through engaging and inspiring adults and young people directly with science and technology, and their implications.

The BA organises major initiatives across the UK, including the annual BA Festival of Science, National Science Week and an extensive programme for children and young people. These include 'First Investigators' which has fun, practical science activities to inspire five to eight year olds, and 'Young Investigators' which aims to develop science investigation skills in 8 to 13 year olds.

National Science Week takes place annually in mid March. It is an opportunity for people of all ages to celebrate science and its importance to our lives by enabling local communities to take part in science, engineering and technology activities.

The Basic Skills Agency

The Basic Skills Agency's goal is to help raise standards of literacy, numeracy and language across all age groups, from cradle to grave. Their three priorities are:

- improving speaking and listening skills
- supporting basic skills at transition points, such as starting school or a new job
- engaging people disengaged from learning.

The Agency has programmes which are aimed at young parents, parents of children from birth to three, grandparents and young children with little or no pre-school experience.

Step in to Learning

Step in to Learning is a front line worker training and development programme designed for staff working in the Early Years and Childcare sector.

It aims to train staff to identify parents/carers and other staff with a literacy, numeracy and/or language need and then encourage and signpost them to take up appropriate local learning opportunities to improve these skills.

To find out where the training will be delivered in your area please visit www.stepintolearning.org or call 01223 478288.

Resources and equipment

The Exploring Together family workshops have been designed to use everyday materials and simple equipment. Good quality magnifiers, pippetes, petri dishes and observation trays are available from Reflections on Learning. For a catalogue ring 01732 225850 or visit www.reflectionsonlearning.co.uk

Sci Tot Exploring Together

This project, funded by a grant from Copus, happened in two phases. Phase 1 involved a series of family workshops run by Linda Thornton and Pat Brunton in Sure Start and early years settings in Cornwall. This was followed in Phase 2 by a dissemination programme in which early years and Sure Start professionals across the South West of England were trained to deliver the Exploring Together family workshop programme.

The evaluation of the two phases of Sci Tot Exploring Together provides some valuable information on the impact of a family learning programme of this nature.

Sci Tot Evaluation - Phase 1

- Response to the workshops was enthusiastic. Of the 46% of family members who returned evaluation questionnaires, 100% said they would participate in another SciTot workshop and 100% said they would recommend these workshops to their friends.
- The workshops succeeded in changing people's attitudes towards science and technology. The 16 participants (42%) who were already enthusiastic continued to be so, but the 22 (58%) who were initially negative or ambivalent all changed their minds after participating in the workshops.
- Parents and family members all said they appreciated the opportunity to investigate scientific and technological concepts alongside their children.
- SciTot workshops provide a good opportunity to involve fathers in their children's learning.
- All participants enjoyed the range of activities presented and everyone took away at least one idea that they would try at home with their children.

Sci Tot Evaluation - Phase 2

- The training events were very enthusiastically received. The detailed planning information and the simple nature of the resources needed to run the workshops encouraged a high level take up of the scheme.
- Many respondents described ways in which they intended to mainstream the Sci Tot workshop activities into their ongoing programme of family support sessions.
- From the comments received there is good evidence that the project has led to an increase in the skills and confidence of early years practitioners in the broad area of science and technology.
- Parents and other family members found the workshops interesting and enjoyable and became more confident in their ability to explore and investigate alongside their children.
- Many parents remarked on the value of activities which used everyday materials. They appreciated the fact that these provided a cheap, easily sourced range of interesting things to do with their children at home.
- Parents and practitioners alike found that family workshops of this nature provide an interesting and enjoyable starting point for involving parents in their children's learning.

More books by Pat Brunton and Linda Thornton

Taking the Lead

Book + CD

A careful review of the aspects of management key to the successful delivery of integrated services for families and young children. Examples are set in the context of managing childcare, early education and family services within the framework of Every Child Matters. Benefits and challenges of managing teams of professionals from diverse backgrounds are recognised, as are the realities of successful team/partnership working. Covers areas of expertise defined within the Common Core of Skills and Knowledge for the Children's Workforce.

ISBN 1905019378

Includes CD of management information and resources.

Little Books with *BIG* Ideas®

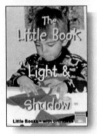

Light & Shadow

Order LB25

Ideas for lots of things for children to do as they explore the wonder of light and the magic of the dark. All use ready-to-hand materials, and no scientific knowledge is needed.

ISBN 1904187811

Time & Place

Order LB31

Ideas for helping children in knowledge and understanding of the world by exploring who they are, where they live, and how people and places change.

ISBN 1904187951

Living Things

Order LB37

Looking at and looking after living things is an important feature of childhood. This book will help you with activities to use in your setting and for expeditions in your local area.

ISBN 1905019122

Treasure Boxes

Order LB47

Treasureboxes are collections of ordinary objects that encourage children to investigate and explore. Children's curiosity, creativity and communication will all be stimulated by following the ideas in this book.

ISBN 1905019491

All the above are available by mail order from

Featherstone Education Ltd, PO Box 6350, Lutterworth LE17 6ZA.
tel.0185 888 1212, fax.0185 888 1360, sales@featherstone.uk.com,
online from www.featherstone.uk.com

or from your usual book supplier.